HAPPINESS IS A SAD SONG

BY

CHARLES M. SCHULZ

SCHOLASTIC BOOK SERVICES

NEW YORK • TORONTO • LONDON • AUCKLAND • SYDNEY • TOKYO

appiness
is waking up, looking
at the clock and finding
that you still have
two hours left to sleep.

appiness

is

a side dish

of

French-fries.

appiness

is

a new sweatshirt

on a cold

Saturday morning.

appiness

is

winning an argument

with

your sister.

appiness

is

having

something

to look forward to.

Happiness
is
the best seat
at
the parade.

appiness

is having

the bell ring

just as you are

being called on to recite.

appiness

is

a

big

muscle.

Happiness is loving your enemies.

appiness

is hearing

the pediatrician say,

"No, I guess she won't

have to have a shot."

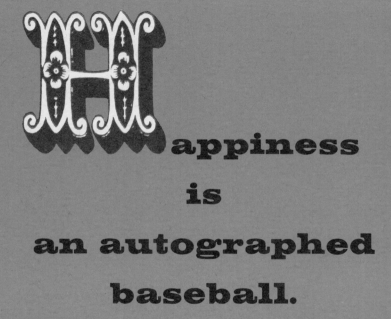

Happiness

is

an autographed

baseball.

appiness

is

being tickled

under

the chin.

appiness

is

coming home

from

the hospital.

appiness

is

a

circus

balloon.

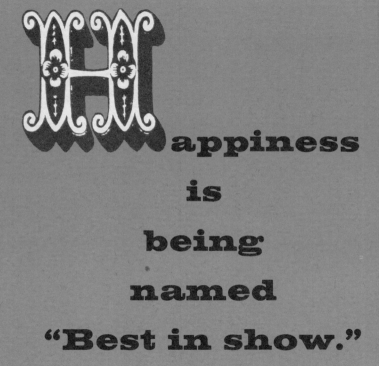

Happiness is being named "Best in show."

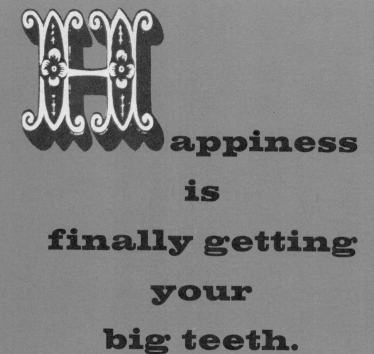

Happiness
is
finally getting
your
big teeth.

Happiness
is
a stack
of
old comic books.

appiness

is

a Christmas vacation

with

no book reports to write.

appiness

is

catching snowflakes

on

your tongue.

appiness

is surprising your Dad

by shoveling the

sidewalk

before he gets home.

appiness

is

licking

the

bowl.

Happiness
is
playing cards
with
Grandma.

Happiness
is sleeping
in the back seat
on
the way home.

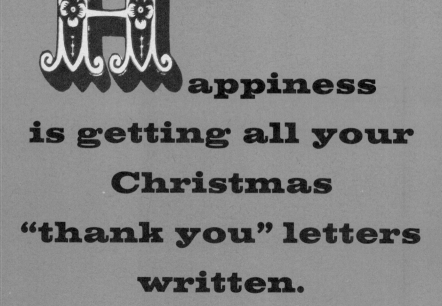

Happiness
is getting all your
Christmas
"thank you" letters
written.

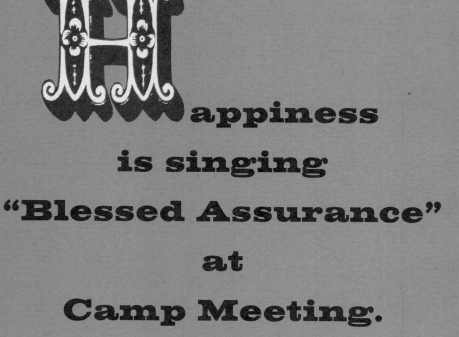

Happiness
is singing
"Blessed Assurance"
at
Camp Meeting.

appiness

is

wearing the band

from

your Dad's cigar.

appiness

is being

too sick to go to school,

but not too sick

to watch T.V.

**appiness is being able to walk home from school without having to worry about getting beaten up.**

appiness

is

a

sad

song.

appiness

is

knowing

you've made it

through one more day.